Copyright © 1998 by Scholastic Inc.
The activities on pages 28–32 copyright © 1998 by Marilyn Burns.
All rights reserved. Published by Scholastic Inc.
Printed in the U.S.A.

ISBN 0-439-69317-9

5 6 7 8 9 10   23   12 11 10 09 08 07

Tic-Tac-Toe
Three in a Row

by Judith Bauer Stamper
Illustrated by Ken Wilson-Max
Math Activities by Marilyn Burns

SCHOLASTIC INC.
New York Toronto London Auckland Sydney
Mexico City New Delhi Hong Kong Buenos Aires

I'm so smart.
Now I know
how to play
tic-tac-toe!

Make an X,
then an O.

Three across.
Tic-tac-toe!

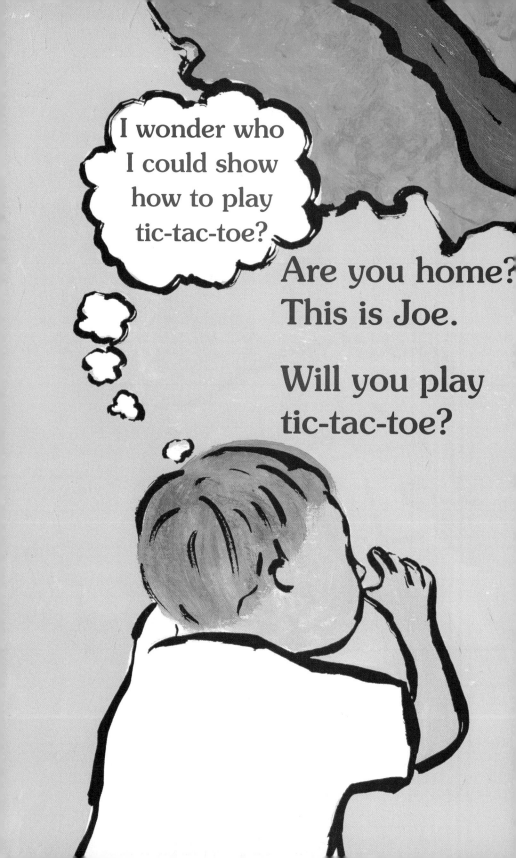

Who is there?
Well, hello.

I like to play
tic-tac-toe.

You go first.
Don't be slow.

I play fast.
Tic-tac-toe.

X, X, X. That's a row—
up and down. Tic-tac-toe.

Try again. Now you go.
Think about tic-tac-toe.

Three more X's.
No, no, no!

You won again.
Tic-tac-toe.

If you want,
I could show
you the rules.
Tic-tac-toe.

Start on top,
or below.
Take your time.
Tic-tac-toe.

Three across—
that's a row.

X, X, X.
Tic-tac-toe.

Up and down,
O, O, O,

also works.
Tic-tac-toe.

Here's another
way to go—

side to side.
Tic-tac-toe.

Thanks a lot!
Now I know
how to play
tic-tac-toe.

Make an X,
then an O.

Will you play
tic-tac-toe?

• ABOUT THE ACTIVITIES •

Tic-tac-toe is a game that fascinates and delights young children. They enjoy figuring out how to draw the tic-tac-toe game board and easily learn how to take turns placing X's or O's. The game also has the benefit of giving children the opportunity to reason logically, an important aspect of mathematical thinking. (As a matter of fact, studying game strategies intrigues many mathematicians and is included in university mathematics courses.)

While learning to play tic-tac-toe isn't difficult for many young children, learning what to do to win or to avoid losing isn't obvious. They need a good deal of time and experience playing the game to figure out how to play strategically.

This book can be enjoyed by children who haven't yet learned about tic-tac-toe as well as by those who already can play the game. The story models the game and shows children different ways to place X's or O's in order to win.

After reading the story with your child, try playing tic-tac-toe together. Then try some of the activities included here. Be open to your child's interests and enjoy the math!

— Marilyn Burns

You'll find tips and suggestions for guiding the activities whenever you see a box like this!

Retelling the Story

Reread the story and look for the tic-tac-toe games as you go.

In the first game, Joe shows his dog how he can win. He made three X's across the top. Point to the winning row of X's.

When Joe plays with the girl, she wins with three X's down the middle. Point to her winning row of X's.

The girl wins again with three X's on a slant. Point to her winning X's.

Then the girl helps Joe win. He makes three X's across the middle. Point to Joe's winning row of X's.

The girl shows Joe how to win by going up and down. Point to the row of O's from top to bottom.

The girl shows Joe another way three O's can go on a slant. Point to the row of O's on a slant.

New vocabulary is best learned in the context of an activity. Use the X's and O's to help your child learn the vocabulary for positions—up, down, left, right, across, on a slant, and so on.

Winning Rows of O's

Here are the eight different ways to win tic-tac-toe with a row of O's. (You could also win the same ways if you put X's where the O's are.)

Half of the ways have an O in the space that is in the middle of the tic-tac-toe board. Find these four boards.